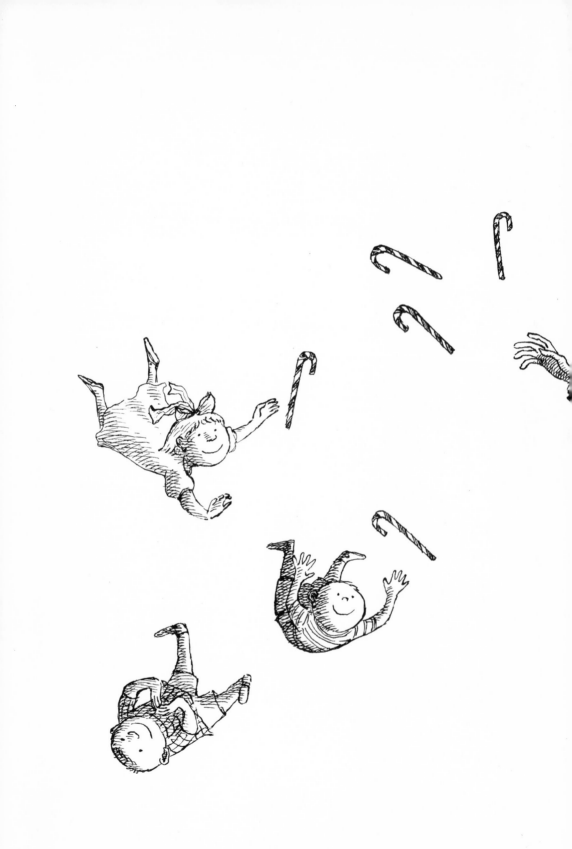

THE MAN WHO SANG THE SILLIES

by John Ciardi

drawings by Edward Gorey

J. B. Lippincott Company · Philadelphia · New York

for
BENN
because he likes poems
and I like him

CONTENTS

THE MAN WHO SANG THE SILLIES

I met a man with a triple-chin.
Whenever he smiled, his chins would grin.
The strangest sight that ever I saw
Was a smile with three grins in its jaw.

"How do you do, do you do, do you do?"
He said to me, "Are you, you, you
Going to come my, come my, come my way?
Be quick for I haven't all day, day, day."

"I'll be happy to come, come, come," said I.
"Young man," said he, "will you tell me why
You have to say everything three times over?
It's a very bad habit, you'll discover."

"I'm sorry," I said, "I . . . I . . . I . . ." "Hush!
It's time for the singing. We'll have to rush.
This way!—Come along, come along, come along."
And off he ran as he sang this song:

Oh, The Sillies are the sweetest that I know:
    They have grins as big as tickles,
    They have titters up their sleeves,
    They make faces dill as pickles,
    And they spin like autumn leaves.
    They have cheeks as red as cherry,
    And they're always losing shoes,
    But they're very very very very
    Easy to amuse.
    You need only call their names
    And they start their giggle games.
    They go scramble-clatter-thump across the floor.
    They go tumble-flopping in and out the door.
    What a screech and clatter! What a roar!
But I always think when it comes time to go
That The Sillies are the sweetest that I know.

Yes, The Sillies are the sweetest that I know.
　　They're a nuisance, they're a bother.
　　They're an everlasting noise.
　　Sillies act like one another.
　　Sillies act like girls and boys.
　　Sillies think it's necessary
　　Not to like what they are fed.
　　They are very very very very
　　Hard to put to bed.
　　You need only say "Bedtime . . . "
　　And they run away and climb
　　Up the chimney, up a moonbeam, out of sight.
　　Till they're caught and snuggled tight.
　　Then they yawn and say "Goodnight . . . . "
　　And their voices are so soft away and slow,
That I have to think when it comes time to go
That The Luckies are The Happies, and The Happies are The Sillies,
And The Sillies are the sweetest that I know.

THE STRANGER IN THE PUMPKIN

The stranger in the pumpkin said:
"It's all dark inside your head.
What a dullard you must be!
Without light how can you see?
Don't you know that heads should shine
From deep inside themselves—like mine?
Well, don't stand there in a pout
With that dark dome sticking out—
It makes me sick to look at it!
Go and get your candle lit!"

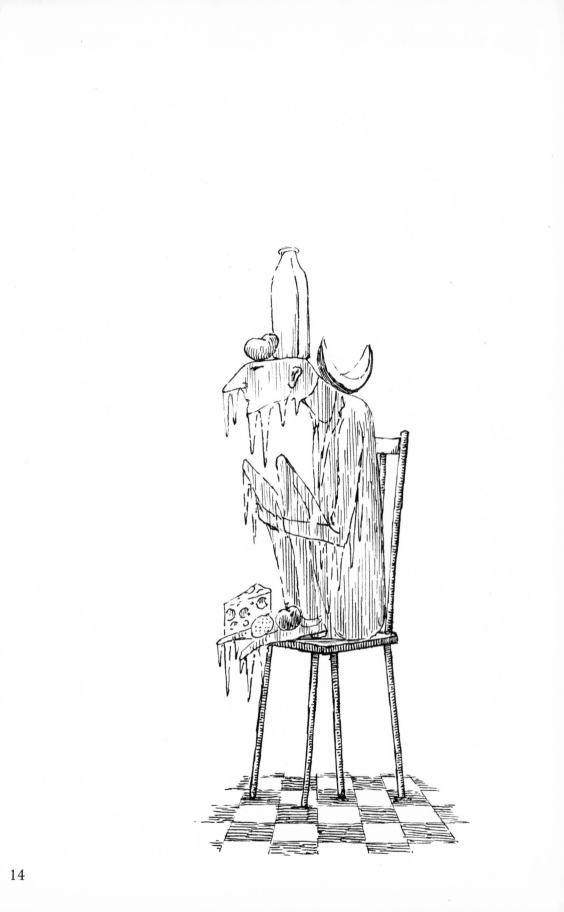

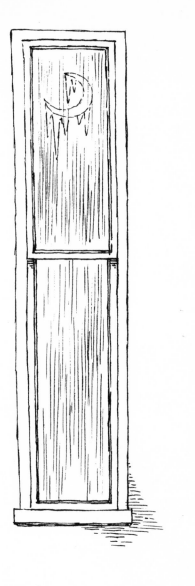

THERE WAS AN OLD MAN

There was an old man, an old, old, old,
    A very old man was he, sir.
All day long he felt cold, cold, cold.
    At night he felt like a freezer.

AS I WAS PICKING A BOBBLE-BUD

As I was picking a bobble-bud
    Out in the bangle-thicket,
A Crow with a voice the color of mud
    Lit on a croquet wicket.

"Hang the mallet and pull the stakes
    And clear the lawn for wishing.
The Needles are bringing prickle-cakes,
    And all the Threads are fishing."

But I was after a bobble-bud
    There in the bangle thicket,
And though his voice was the color of mud
    I would not buy a ticket.

"Be hanged to your mallet and stakes," I said.
    "Be hanged to your voice like mud.
I've yet to see the Needle or Thread
    That's worth a bobble-bud.

A bobble-bud will not be sewn:
    You wear it in your heart.
And once you do you're never alone,
    Though the world be miles apart.

It wants no ticket, it wants no crowing,
    It wants no prickle-cakes or fish.
And once it's in your heart and growing,
    It's all there is in the world to wish."

SAY YES TO THE MUSIC, OR ELSE

What I have to say of Clarence Fud
(Who wouldn't say yes and wouldn't say no) is:
Once you turn into a stick-in-the-mud,
You can't be sure where your big toe is.

Suppose it itches, suppose it twitches
And wants to go where the music goes?
—If you're stuck in the mud like Clarence Fud
You can't get the music into your toes.

Say yes to the music when it tickles.
Or else—well, just remember Clarence,
Whose toes turned into ten dill pickles.
That was a terrible blow to his parents.

Imagine having to say to your son,
"Be sure to wash your pickles, dear."
That shouldn't happen to anyone.
Not even to parents. But never fear—

Say *yes* to the music when it tickles
And when you come to wash your toes,
You'll never find them changed to pickles.
That's the way the music goes.

SYLVESTER

Sylvester wrote to Mary Lou.
Said, "Will you marry me?"
Replied a Lady Kangaroo,
"My darling, I agree."

"Agree to what?" Sylvester cried.
"I've never before seen *you!*"
"Well, no," the Kangaroo replied,
"But though *that's* perfectly true,

Here is your letter sent to me."
"To *you!* Don't be absurd!"
"Don't tamper with the mails," said she,
"A man must keep his word!"

"My letter was sent to Mary Lou!"
"It came to *me!*" "Agreed.
But you saw it wasn't addressed to you!"
"How could I?—I can't read."

"Then how could you read the letter
But not how it was addressed?"
"I could say your writing got better,
Or I could say I just guessed.

The point is," said the Kangaroo,
"—And the mailman will agree—
Whatever you wrote to Mary Lou,
The letter came to *me.*

You must either learn to write what you mean
Or to mean what you write!" she cried.
"And though I'd rather not make a scene,
I insist you must make me your bride!"

"We'll just see about that," said Sylvester. "No doubt
We will," said the Kangaroo.
—And how do you think it all turned out?
—I only wish I knew.

JERRY MULLIGAN

Jerry Mulligan came to see me,
    Dropped his cap in the chowder pot,
Put it on as he was leaving,
    Said, "My word! It's getting hot!"

Good fish chowder! good clam chowder!
    Makes you want to cry for more!
Three fat clams behind his ears,
    Jerry started out the door.

Three fat fish heads, four fat fishtails,
    Five grey squids with forty toes,
Six sea dollars, seven crab shells
    Trickled down his hair and nose.

"It's getting foggy out!" said Jerry,
    "Well, goodbye"—and shook my hand
Just as a wave rolled down his sleeve
    And left me holding a ton of sand.

Good fish chowder! good clam chowder!
Makes you want to shout for more!
Fills you up from toe to cap, sir!
Makes you hear the ocean roar!

Eight small whales will fill a kettle.
Nine large barnacles will not.
Where do all the oceans empty?
Into my big black chowder pot.

Good fish chowder! good clam chowder!
Anybody seen my shoe?
Nancy put it in the chowder?
I was saving it for the stew!

'Bye, Jerry Mulligan, come again.
But keep your cap on when you do.
The chowder pot can hold a lot
But not as much as you!

Good fish chowder! good clam chowder!
Makes you shout for more and more!
Fills you up from toe to cap, sir!
Makes you hear the ocean roar!

THERE WAS A HUNTER FROM LITTLETOWN

There once was a Hunter from Littletown.
    He made his bullets of sugar cane.
And every duck that he shot down
    Got up and flew away again.

He shot a Lobster out of a tree
    And up it rose again and said:
"Sorry. Which way is the sea?"
    Said the Hunter: "Aren't you dead?"

"Dead?" said the Lobster. "What a thought!
    Why ever should I be dead?"
"I'm sure," said the Hunter, "I heard a shot.
    Would you look for a hole in your head?"

"Do you call that polite?" the Lobster replied.
    "I'll thank you to be more agreeable."
But he put up one claw to his forehead and cried:
    "Oh really, *this* wasn't foreseeable!"

For there *was* a hole, and however he tried
    He couldn't deny it. "Oh mercy on me!"
Wept the Lobster, and promptly rolled over and died.
    Said the Hunter: "You're kind to agree."

And that night at supper his wife picked a claw
    And the Hunter at least two or three,
From the finest fat Lobster that ever you saw
    Shot down from its perch in a tree.

THE MOST OF BEING A BOY IS NOISE

The most of being a boy is NOISE.
SILENCE doesn't do well with boys.
SILENCE and boys, when they happen to meet,
May look at each other across the street,
And maybe they'll even say Hello,
But they always have somewhere else to go.
If SILENCE should happen to stop and play,
Boys are certain to run away.
Or the minute SILENCE sits down with boys,
He looks over his shoulder, and there comes NOISE!

Then he has to cover his ears and run.
And the boys all shriek and think it's fun.
That's what *they* think. And I'll say this:
Most of the time it really is!

SUMMER SONG

By the sand between my toes,
By the waves behind my ears,
By the sunburn on my nose,
By the little salty tears
That make rainbows in the sun
When I squeeze my eyes and run,
By the way the seagulls screech,
Guess where I am? *At the . . . . . !*
By the way the children shout
Guess what happened? *School is . . . . . !*
By the way I sing this song
Guess if summer lasts too long:
You must answer Right or . . . . . !

CHILDREN WHEN THEY'RE VERY SWEET

Children, when they're very sweet,
    Only bite and scratch and kick
A very little. Just enough
    To show their parents they're not sick.

After all if children *should*
    (By some horrible mistake)
Be entirely good all day
    Every parent's heart would ache.

"Our little monsters must be ill:
    They're much too well behaved!
Call the doctor! Do it quick!
    Maybe they can still be saved!

. . . Wait! They're looking better now.
    Johnny just kicked Billy's shin!
Betty just bit Teddy's ear!
    Jane just stuck me with a pin!

There! The little dears are fit
    As sharks and crocodiles, you'll find.
No need for the doctor now:
    Get a stick and make them mind!"

SOME COOK!

Johnny made a custard
In the pepper pot.
Flavored it with mustard,
Put in quite a lot
Of garlic fried in olive oil,
Brought the custard to a boil,
Ate it up and burned his tongue—

You shouldn't cook when you're too young.

LOBSTER MUSIC

There was a man in a Lobster-boat.
    His traps were made of fiddle-strings.
And every Lobster that he caught
    Played him a tune. The middle strings
Were set to play "I'm Bound Away"
    At the scrape of a Lobster's claw.
While the treble would tinkle "Twinkle Twinkle,"
    And the bass "I Dreamed I Saw."

And as soon as he heard the music start
    The Lobster man began to cry.
For the music made him sad at heart,
    Though he didn't exactly know why.
Except that he thought of the Lobster pot
    And the Lobsters bubbling away
With never a song to cheer them along
    And never a tune to play

But "Bubble Bubble, Toil and Trouble"—
    As sad as a tune can be.
"And that is why," he said with a sigh,
    "When I drop my traps in the sea,
I like a song to cheer along
    My pets. And you *will* agree
That it gets too hot when you're in the pot
    For a proper melody.

So sing while you may, I always say,
    And boil when you must, says I,
For a bit of a song is never wrong
    Though you're hoisted high and dry.
And I like a bit of a tune I do
    When Lobsters are on the way—
Boiled and buttered, or in a stew,
    Or cold in a salad for lunch next day."

THE HAPPY FAMILY

Before the children say goodnight,
    Mother, Father, stop and think:
Have you screwed their heads on tight?
    Have you washed their ears with ink?

Have you said and done and thought
    All that earnest parents should?
Have you beat them as you ought?
    Have you begged them to be good?

And above all—when you start
    Out the door and douse the light—
Think, be certain, search your heart:
    Have you screwed their heads on tight?

If they sneeze when they're asleep,
    Will their little heads come off?
If they just breathe very deep?
    If—especially—they cough?

Should—alas!—the little dears
    Lose a little head or two,
Have you inked their little ears:
    Girls' ears pink and boys' ears blue?

Children's heads are very loose.
    Mother, Father, screw them tight.
If you feel uncertain use
    A monkey wrench, but do it right.

If a head should come unscrewed
    You will know that you have failed.
Doubtful cases should be glued.
    Stubborn cases should be nailed.

Then when all your darlings go
    Sweetly screaming off to bed,
Mother, Father, you may know
    Angels guard each little head.

Come the morning you will find
    One by one each little head
Full of gentle thoughts and kind,
    Sweetly screaming to be fed.

TIME

The stars sit still and the world goes round—
    India, Egypt, U.S.A.—
The world keeps turning, the sun comes out.
    And that's the story of every day.

Turn from the East, turn to the West,
    The sun comes out and starts to climb
As high as noon, then down again.
    And that's the story of time.

The stars tell time to the telescope.
    The telescope tells the clock.
The clock tells everyone in the house.
    And that's the story of tick and tock.

If you want to hear the star in the clock
    Go fish one out of the pool.
If you can't do that, you'll have to wait
    Till you learn the stars in school.

But the truth is just what I said it was,
    And just as it has to be,
And just as it always was before,
    And just as they taught it to me—

The stars tell time to the telescope,
    And the telescope tells the clock,
And the clock tells everyone in the house.
    And that's the story of tick and tock.

HOW MUCH IS TRUE?

I'll tell you a lie, and it's almost true:
I met an oyster as big as you.
And boy-size oysters are very few.

Man-size oysters are even fewer.
You see—my lie's getting truer and truer.
That happens to lies, you may be sure:

You start to tell a terrible whopper,
Then all your fibbing comes a cropper,
And your lie winds up all prim and proper.

"Hello!" I said when we met, said I.
The oyster frowned and strolled on by.
(Now have I managed to tell a lie?)

The oyster's name was Snaggletooth.
He had a sister named Bluepoint Ruth.
They lived in a shipwrecked telephone booth.

—How do I know? Well, some I guessed,
And some I imagined, and the rest
My friend, the Oysterman, confessed.

The Oysterman's name is Rocky Ray,
The Champion Mudfoot of Chesapeake Bay.
He told me all this yesterday.

And his tears poured down like the morning tide.
"I stole them out of the sea!" he cried,
"Where they lay all cozy and side by side

In their well-kept shipwrecked telephone booth!
I sold the oyster named Snaggletooth!
And for lunch I had crackers and Bluepoint Ruth!"

That's what he told me—more or less—
And some say no and some say yes,
But true or not is anyone's guess.

—I say I said, "Hello!" said I,
And the oyster frowned and strolled on by.
And it's certainly true that he didn't reply.

He may not have *frowned*. When they come to town,
Oysters, strolling along, look down
With a strange expression. It *could* be a frown,

Or it could be a smile. It's hard to tell
An oyster's expression through his shell
Unless you know him especially well.

—And that's my story. You realize
It's bound to come as a sort of surprise
To meet an oyster of such a size

Just strolling along.—Well, maybe not
Exactly *strolling*. It looked a lot
As if he were strolling, and that's what *I* thought.

At first at least. But it just may be
The strolling was really done by me
And not by the oyster—Yes, certainly:

I remember now! It was where I ate
My lunch today—at Main and State—
And the oyster was on a dinner plate.

An *enormous* plate! And there he sat
As big as you and twice as fat!
—Well, maybe he wasn't as big as *that*.

I guess he was only just oyster-size.
And recalling his taste now, I realize
Oysters go down much better than lies.

And I'll tell you this: I never knew
Lies were *so hard* to make up, sir. And you
May believe it or not, but that's *certainly* true.

THE MAN FROM THE WOODS

The man from the woods
    Climbed out of my well
With some very strange goods
    He wanted to sell.

I was out on the farm
    And all alone
When I saw one arm
    Reach over the stone

Like a brambly shoot
    Or a prickly hedge.
And then one foot
    Grew over the edge,

Like roots when they grow
    Along the ground.
It frightened me so
    I turned around

And started to run,
    But he started to sing
In a voice like a pun
    With a quibbledy ring.

A two-tone voice
      Like a brook on a hill.
It was half just noise,
      And half bird-trill:

"Come buy, come buy what I have to sell.
      What's deepest, darkest, and longest gone
Out of the sun and down through the well
      To the little dark places in stone.

I have veins of iron and dusts of gold.
      Moss cake, root hair, beetle shell.
The last ball Rip Van Winkle bowled.
      And somewhere the first as well.

I have mildew glue and limestone twists.
      Darks of caves and water sound.
Bat-fur, fox-fire, mandrake fists.
      And all the lost buttons that no one has found.

I have rattlesnake rattles and dinosaur bone.
      Hearts of sulfur and mushroom seed.
Good fern jelly and honey stone.
      Come buy whatever you need."

He sang so small
      And so far and near,
And his voice was all
      So muffled and clear,

So twice-at-once,
      As I think I've said,
That I felt like a dunce
      For being afraid.

So I turned around
    To see his face.
—And there wasn't a sound!
    There wasn't a trace!

Whoever he was,
    He had been and gone.
But there on the grass
    Was a milk-white stone.

And as red a rose
    As ever grew.
Though I don't suppose
    You'll believe it's true.

MARGARET NASH GOT WET
BUT I DON'T KNOW HOW

Margaret Nash
Went swimming—splash!—
Right in the middle of the Ocean.
"What? Swimming where?
Who took her there?"
—I haven't the slightest notion.

She jumped from a ship
And cut her lip
According to the Squid.
She fell from a plane
That was going to Spain.
That's what Fish say she did.

She fell from a cloud
She wasn't allowed—
Except in dreams—to ride.
It changed to rain
And she couldn't remain.
Or so I'm told by the Tide.

She paddled on toast
Away from the coast
According to the Whale.
The toast soaked thin.
Margaret fell in.
—But what an unlikely tale!

What a pack of lies;
It's just not wise
To trust what you hear in the Ocean.
And truth to tell
The fact is—well,
I haven't the slightest notion.

EVAN KIRK

Evan Kirk
Is looking for work.
Work? What can he do?
He could milk a cow
If he just knew how.
He can almost buckle a shoe.

He can count to ten
Again and again
With hardly a real mistake.
He could drive a bus
If one of us
Would handle the wheel and the brake.

He can climb a chair
When no one's there
And reach where the cookies are.
He can catch you frogs
And pollywogs
At eleven cents a jar.

For a nickel a day
He will hammer away
At woodwork, walls, and doors.
Or for nothing at all
He will paint the hall
And nail down all your floors.

The little dear
Has been working here
A year—well, almost two.
And you couldn't foresee
How glad we'd be
To send him to work on you.

IT'S TIME TO GET UP

The sun's in the window, and who do you guess
    Is still pretending she doesn't know
I've come to call her to wash and dress
    And come to breakfast? Jenny?—No.

Ginny? Mary? Sally-Lou?
    It's none of those, but I see a head
With one eye peeking—I think I do—
    And someone's giggling in that bed.

Who do you guess it would have to be?
    It isn't I—I'm already dressed.
And mother's downstairs, so it couldn't be she.
    And there's nobody else but—ah, you guessed!

That's my buzzard! as bright as beans!
    Flap your wings and away we go!
We have waffles as crunchy as window screens,
    And shredded rope to help you grow,

And rubber-band pudding with raisins and nails,
    And seventeen kinds of Preposterous-meat,
Including the horns, and the hooves, and the scales—
    So toss back those covers and come down and eat.

For the sun's in the window, a bird's on the sill,
    And the wind's in the top of a tree
Singing, "Oh what a shame to be lying there still,
    When it's time to be playing with me!"

WARNING

The inside of a whirlpool
Is not a place to stop,
Or you'll find you reach the bottom
Before you reach the top.

PLEASE, JOHNNY!

The SHREEK is a shiverous beast.
    He's as loud as a boy-and-a-half.
All other beasts shun him—at least
    When he lets out that boomerous laugh.

When he whispers, it sounds like the roar
    Of a train on a bridge you are under.
When he talks, it sounds very much more
    Like a cave full of cannons a-thunder.

But not even the last clap of doom
    Could be heard through his blabberous laugh.
Nothing human could live through its boom.
    It's as loud as a boy-and-a-half.

TWO LESSONS

I.

A frightful Scowl
Met an Owl
Sitting in a tree.
The Owl said, "who?"
—If it was you
Who answered, "It is me,"

Then hide your face.
You're in disgrace.
And the next time you reply
To a bird in a tree
Don't say, "It's me."
Say, properly, "It is I."

II.

People who say NOOZ for NEWS
Must think that kittens' cries are MOOS.
Kittens, properly, say MEW,
Rhyming it, properly, with YOU.

SIZES

If you were as big as a giant flea,
How much would you have to grow to be
The size of the tiniest head-to-tail
Very most midgety baby whale?

I mean to say—and it's no surprise—
Whatever you do about your size,
There's always something a size or two
Very much bigger or smaller than you.

I mean to say, what's big of some
Is small of others. Now get along home.
And whether you stay or wander far,
Be just the size of whatever you are.

SOMEONE'S FACE

Someone's face was all frowned shut,
    All squeezed full of grims and crinkles,
Pouts and scowls and gloomers, but
    I could see behind the wrinkles—

Even with her face a-twist,
    I saw Someone peeking through.
And when Someone's nose was kissed,
    Guess who came out giggling?—YOU!